Enzo ...
the Park

Written by Diana Kimpton

Illustrated by Georgie Birkett

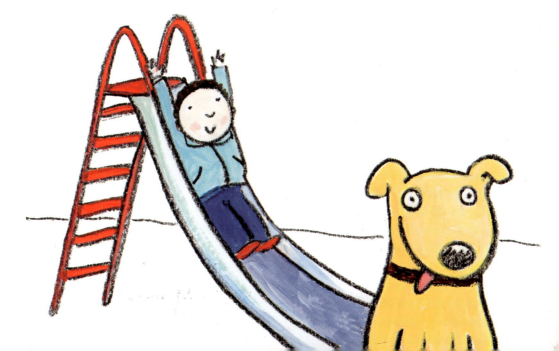

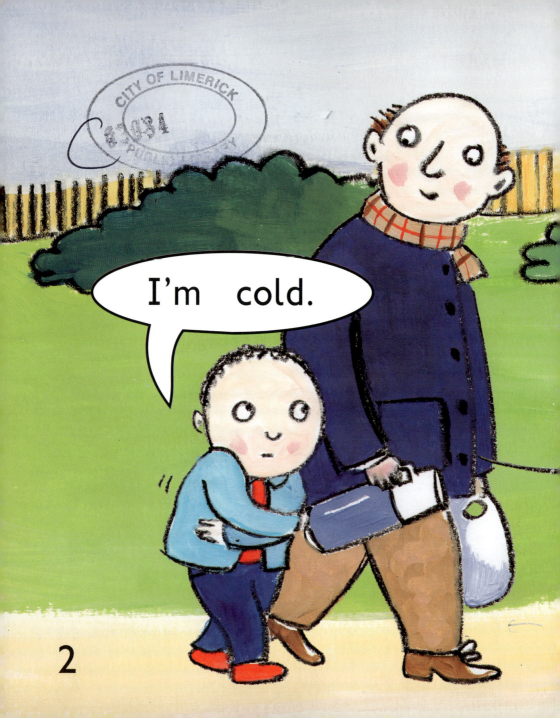

2

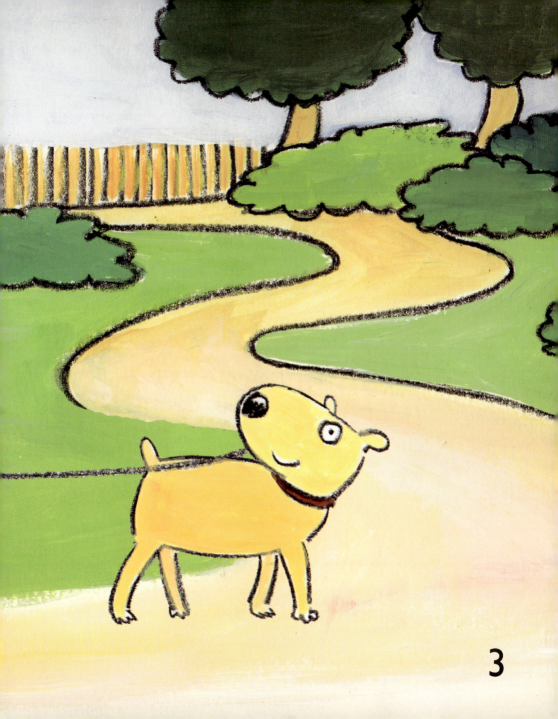

3

Enzo played on the swing.

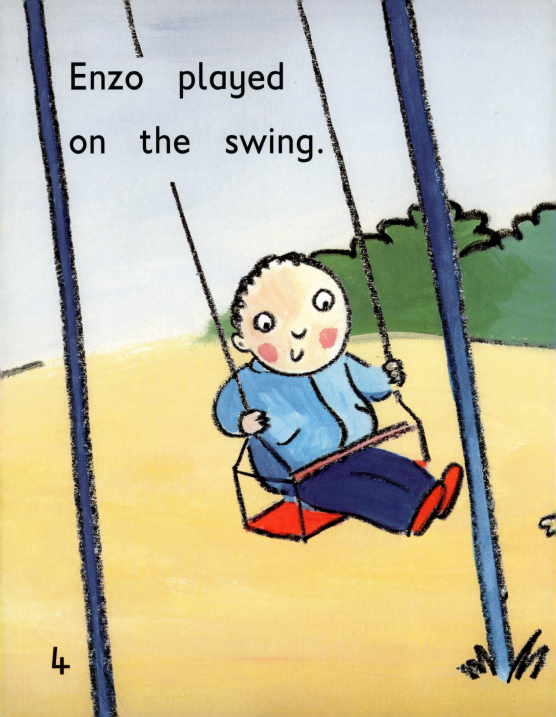

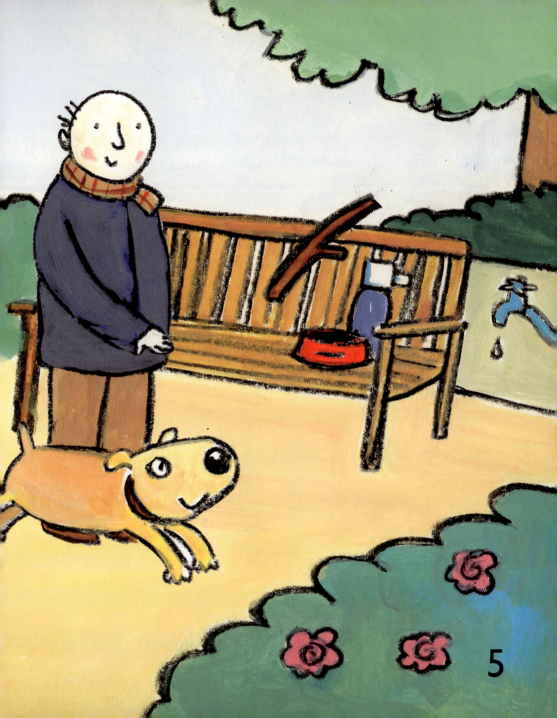

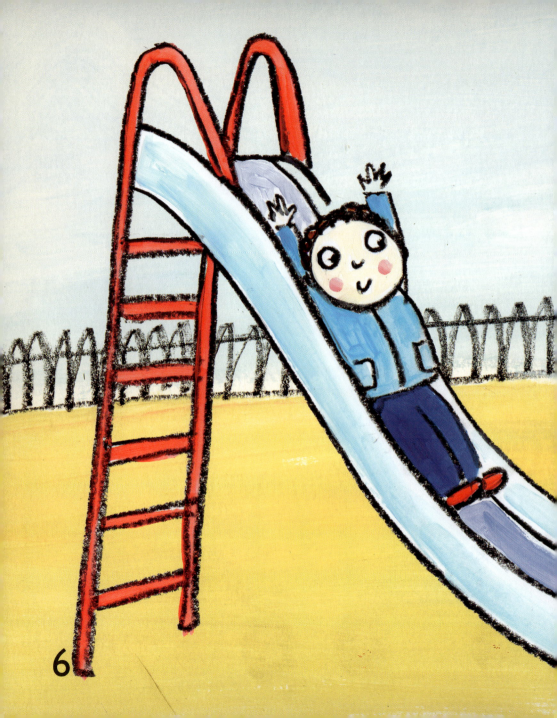

6

Enzo played
on the slide.

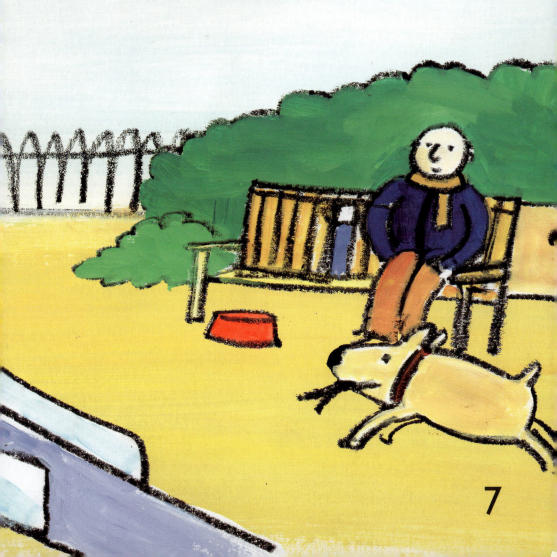

Enzo played
on the roundabout.

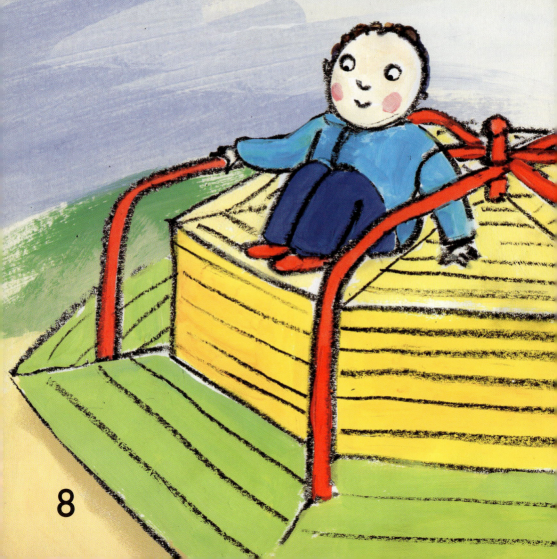

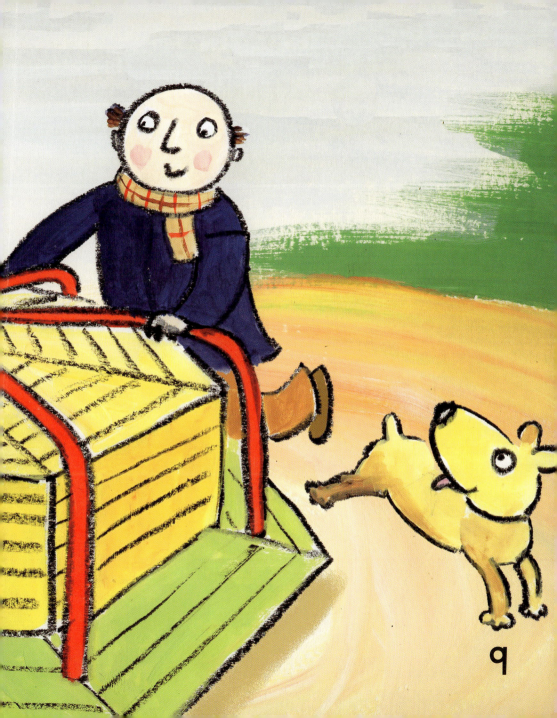

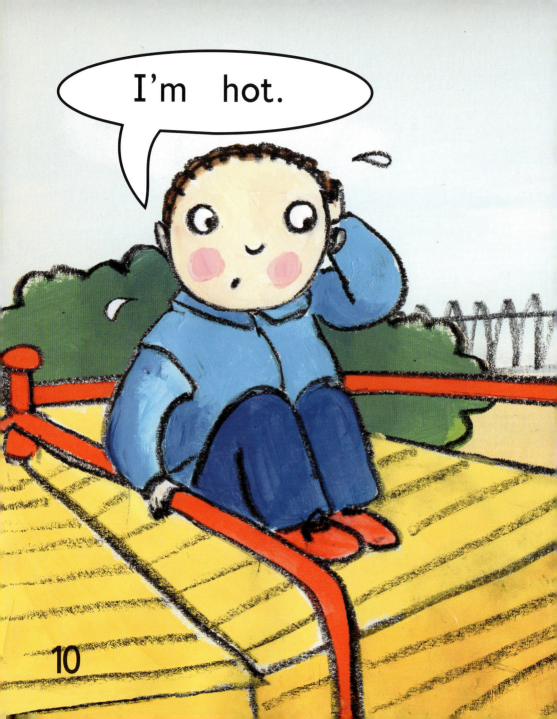

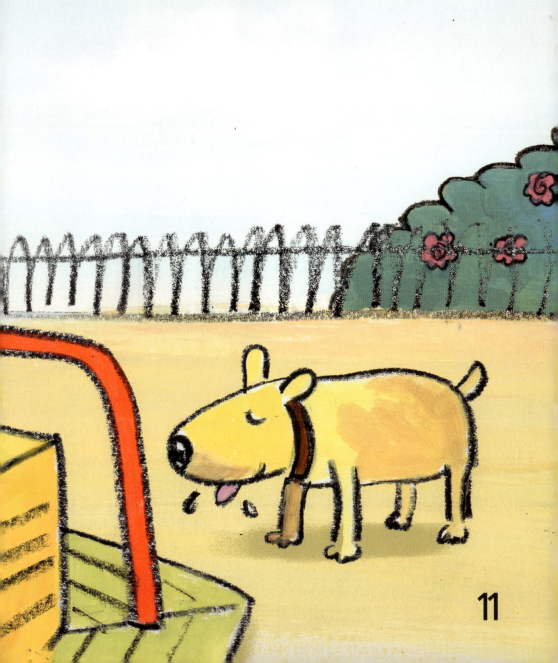

11

Enzo sat on the bench.

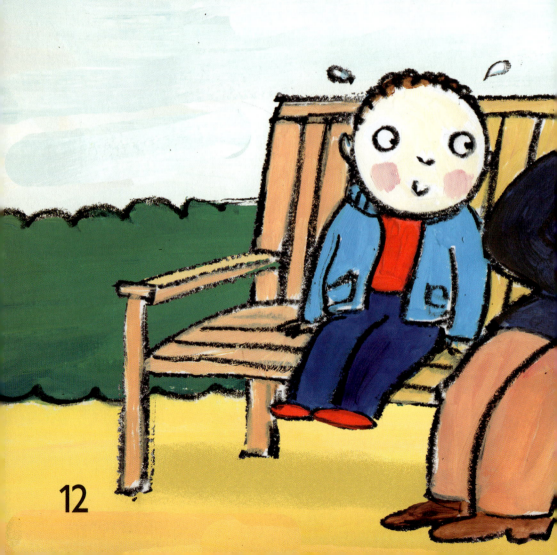

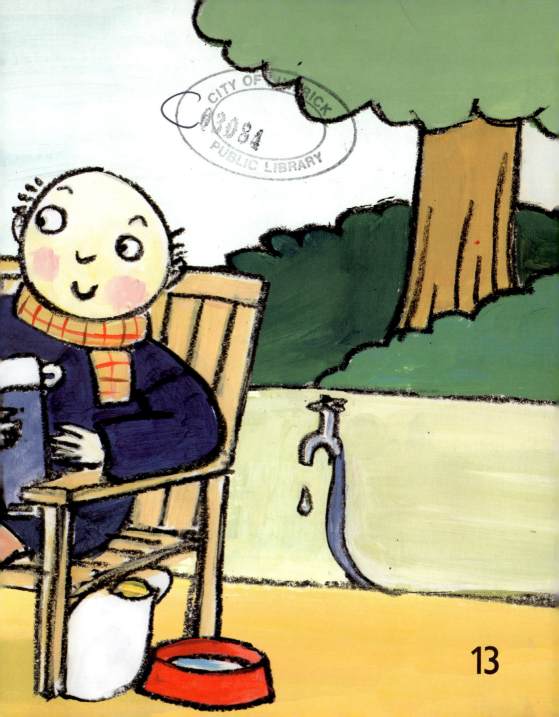

13

Enzo had a drink.

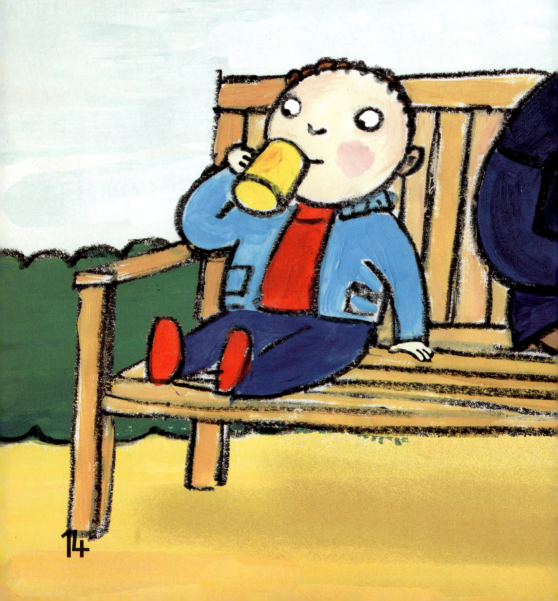

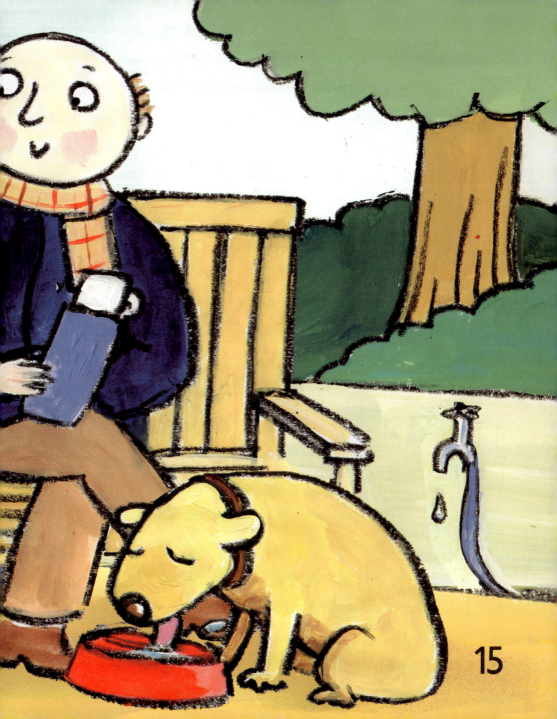

15

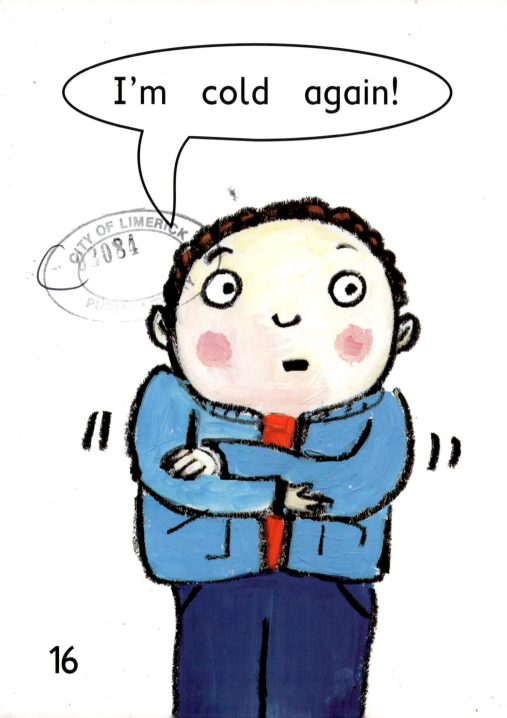